C000170525

Contents

Halley Court, Jordan Hill, Oxford, OX2 8EJ
a division of Harcourt Education Ltd

www.myprimary.co.uk

Help and support for teachers, plus the widest
range of education solutions

Rigby is a registered trademark of Harcourt
Education Ltd

Fearful and Foolish first published 2004

'The Flying Head' © Harcourt Education Limited
2004

'The Three Magicians' © Harcourt Education
Limited 2004

'Mighty Thor and the Magic Hammer' © Harcourt
Education Limited 2004

Series editor: Shirley Bickler

08 07 06 05

10 9 8 7 6 5 4 3

Fearful and Foolish
ISBN 0433 034947

Group reading pack with teaching notes
ISBN 0433 035617

Illustrated by Richard Johnson, Anne Wilson
and Seb Burnett

Cover illustration © Gabrielle Barnes

Designed by StoreyBooks

Repro by Digital Imaging, Glasgow

Printed and bound in China by CTPS

The Flying Head

A Native American Tale

retold by **Rosalind Kerven**

illustrated by **Richard Johnson**

Fearful and Foolish

Once a woman went for a walk through
the forest. The sun was setting and the
trees were full of shadows.

Suddenly, she heard a strange noise
behind her:

Flip-flap

Flip-flap

She turned her head to see what it was –
and screamed.

6

There, behind her, was a monster! It
was the strangest, most horrible thing the
woman had ever seen. It had no arms.
It had no legs. It didn't even have a body.
It was just a big, fat, grinning head
with wings.

"Who ... who are you?" whispered the woman. "What do you want?"

"I am the Flying Head," said the monster. It opened its mouth wide. The woman could see its sharp teeth.

"I'm hungry," it said. "I want to eat you."

"No!" screamed the woman, and she backed away. The Flying Head came after her.

The poor woman was shaking all over. Quickly, she pulled some bread out of her bag and threw it onto the ground behind her. "Eat this instead," she called.

The Flying Head swooped down, took the bread and gobbled it up.

9

"Very tasty," said the Flying Head. "But I still want to eat *you*."

The woman pulled a blanket from her bag and threw it at the Flying Head. The blanket got tangled in its wings.

The Flying Head yelled and struggled, and the woman took her chance! She ran to a tree, climbed up it and hid deep in the branches.

The Flying Head soon got free of the blanket. It flew angrily round and round the tree. "I'm coming to get you!" it called. "I'm coming to eat you!"

But it couldn't reach the woman, so it flapped to the bottom of the tree and waited. She was trapped!

12

Time went by. At last the woman heard the Flying Head snoring. It was asleep. She slid down the tree. She pulled some rope from her bag and tied the Flying Head to the tree trunk. Then she ran home.

13

The woman ran inside her house and shut the door. Was she safe at last? No, she wasn't! Once again, she heard that noise:

Flip-flap

Flip-flap

The Flying Head was free and it was coming after her!

The Flying Head pushed the door open. It hung there in the doorway, gnashing its teeth and grinning. "I'm hungry," it said. "I want to eat you!"

Whatever could the woman do?

15

Suddenly, she had an idea. "You can eat me," she said, "but you need to cook me first. I'll help you."

She put one hand behind her back. Then, with her other hand, she picked up a big stone and threw it into the cooking fire.

"There," she said. "I'm roasting my hand for you. I'll tell you when it's ready."

Time went by.

"Is that hand cooked yet?" asked the Flying Head.

The woman peered into the cooking fire. The stone was red-hot. "Yes," she said. "It's ready now. Come and get it!"

17

The Flying Head swooped down to the cooking fire. It opened its mouth and grabbed the red-hot stone.

"Ow!" it screamed. "AAHHH! It's hot!" Its lips sizzled. Its mouth steamed. Its wings flapped.

The Flying Head spun round and round. Then, still screaming, it zoomed out and away over the forest.

After that, the Flying Head was never seen again.

19

The Three Magicians

A folk tale from Ethiopia

retold by Rosalind Kerven

illustrated by Anne Wilson

One day, three magicians got talking.

"I'm the greatest magician!" cried the first one. "I can work better spells than you two!"

"Huh!" said the second magician. "I bet they're not as clever as *mine*!"

The third magician snorted. "Just wait till you see *my* spells," he said. "They're the best in the world!"

"There's only one thing for it," said the first magician. "We must have a competition. Let's each take turns to work some magic, to see who is the cleverest."

"Good idea," said the other two.

The first magician pointed down the road. A pile of big, white bones lay there, gleaming in the sun.

"Let's try our magic on those bones," he said.

"Hold on," said the second magician. "That looks like a dead lion to me."

"So it is," said the third magician. "That's just what we need for our competition. Who's brave enough to bring the lion back to life?"

"Me!" said the first magician. "I'm not scared. I want to go first."

He stepped forward and held his stick over the pile of lion bones. He took a deep breath and shouted:

"Bing bong! Don't be long!

Join up bones, nice and strong."

At once the bones all jumped up and stuck themselves together – and there was the skeleton of a lion!

"I don't think much of that trick," said the second magician. "You've only stuck the bones together, my friend. It still doesn't look like a real lion. I can do much better than that. Watch!"

27

The second magician took his stick and waved it over the lion skeleton. He shouted:

"Dogs bark, cats purr.

Give this lion a coat of fur!"

At once the bones filled out with flesh. Then the flesh was covered with skin. After that, the skin grew a thick coat of fur. Now it really did look like a lion!

The third magician laughed.

"Your spells are rubbish!" he said. "That lion's still dead. It's lucky that my magic is much stronger than yours. Watch!"

The third magician did a dance all
around the lion. Then he threw his stick into
the air and caught it. He twirled it round
the lion's head and shouted:

"Ten! Six! Three! Five!

Make this lion come alive!"

At first nothing happened.

But then... the lion twitched.

It blinked.

It began to breathe.

Then, it stood up and stretched! It stared round at the three magicians with its big yellow eyes. It opened its mouth and gave a great YAWN!

"I've won!" cried the third magician. "I brought this lion back to life!"

"Huh!" said the second magician. "Your magic wouldn't have worked without *mine*. I made it look like a proper lion."

"But it was *my* spells that joined the bones together in the first place," said the first magician.

And the three magicians carried on shouting and arguing about whose magic was best.

They got so angry, they forgot all about the lion. But the lion certainly didn't forget about them!

33

The lion walked round and round the three magicians. It sniffed them carefully. It licked its lips. It dribbled with greed. It gave a great ROAR!

34

Then it jumped on the three silly
magicians …

35

... and gobbled them all up!

Mighty Thor and the Magic Hammer

written by Jane Langford

illustrated by Seb Burnett

This story is about Thor, his father, his friends Loki and Freya, and a great, big ugly giant.

I am the god of Thunder!

Thor

Odin

I am Thor's father. I am the King of gods!

One day, Thor came thundering home over the Rainbow Bridge.

My hammer! My hammer! I've lost my mighty hammer!

Thor stormed into the palace and clapped his hands. Lightning flew from his iron gloves.

I have lost my hammer!

Quickly! Search the palace everyone!

We must find the hammer!

Thor's mighty hammer was not just any hammer.
It was a magic hammer.

It kills an army with one blow!

It brings calm to the world.

We are lost without it!

It keeps the world in order.

Thor and his servants looked for the hammer all day and all night. But no one found it.

Hurry! Hurry! WE MUST FIND IT!

Thor was angry. Thunder rumbled and lightning flashed. At last a servant ran into the palace.

My Lord! I have seen the hammer!

Tell us! Tell us! Where is it?

Yes, where?

44

Fearful and Foolish

Loki argued with the giant. But it was no good.

Thor told Freya what the Frost Giant wanted.

Give myself to the Frost Giant? Never!

Freya, you must go! We must have the mighty hammer. The world is lost without it.

Then get it yourself! I will never be the Frost Giant's wife!

52

SLAM!

Odin and Thor talked all night. The cold moon came and went.

All is lost! We will never get the mighty hammer back.

We MUST get it back. We must find a way.

As dawn broke, Loki ran outside.

Thor! Odin! I have a plan!

What? What is it?

Tell me! Quickly!

Everyone looked at Thor.

Who? Me? But I am a god! I'm not going to wear a dress!

Thor stormed around the palace for hour after hour.

What can I do?

56

But Thor could not think of a better idea. When the sun sat high in the sky, he gave in.

Put this on.

And this.

Grrrrr!

Wear my special necklace. The Frost Giant knows that it is mine.

Then the Frost Giant wanted to kiss Freya.

Come, let me kiss you.

What! Who? Me? Never!

Er... no. You can kiss her later. First you must give me the hammer.

The Frost Giant couldn't wait any longer. He wanted to kiss the lovely Freya now. So he called his servants.

Fetch the hammer. Quickly!

The servants brought the hammer on a beautiful shiny silver plate.

At last! Here is Thor's mighty hammer.

At last! The hammer is ours again.

Thor and Loki ran back to their palace. The hammer was safe. The Frost Giant had a very sore head. And Thor never had to wear a dress again!